HARDY BOYS
MYSTERY MAZES
by VLADIMIR KOZIAKIN

tempo
books

GROSSET & DUNLAP
A FILMWAYS COMPANY
Publishers • New York

All Rights Reserved
ISBN: 0-448-14508-1
A Tempo Books Original
Tempo Books is registered in the U.S. Patent Office
Published simultaneously in Canada
Printed in the United States of America

HOW TO SOLVE HARDY BOYS MYSTERY MAZES

Here are 20 mysterious mazes, all taken from the famous cases of the Hardy Boys. To solve a maze, take your pencil and start where the arrow points in. Then look for the one, clear path to the exit where the arrow points out. *Do not cross any solid lines!* Solutions begin on page 44.

That's all there is to it, so happy sleuthing!

Vladimir Koziakin

Maze 1
THE MYSTERY OF
THE SPIRAL BRIDGE

Maze 2
THE MYSTERY OF
THE CHINESE JUNK

Maze 3
THE HOODED HAWK MYSTERY

Maze 4
THE MASKED MONKEY

Maze 5
A FIGURE IN HIDING

Maze 6
WHILE THE CLOCK TICKED

Maze 7
THE SIGN OF THE
CROOKED ARROW

Maze 8
MYSTERY AT DEVIL'S PAW

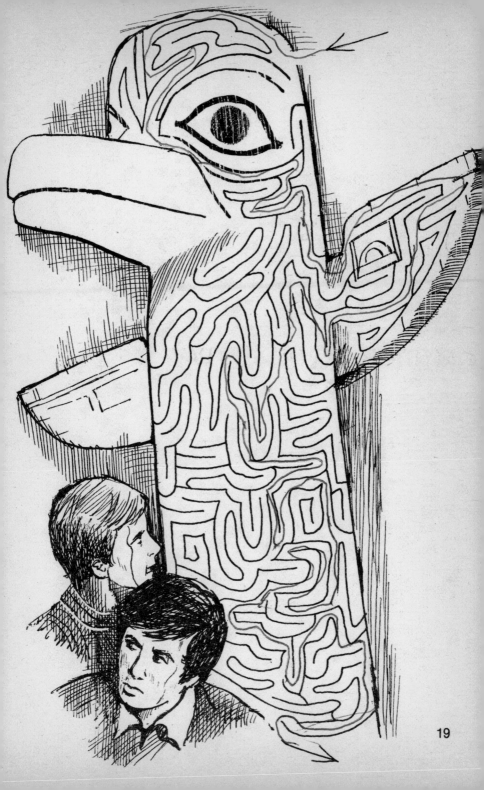

THE SECRET OF PIRATES' HILL

Maze 10
THE SHORE ROAD MYSTERY

Maze 11
THE SINISTER SIGNPOST

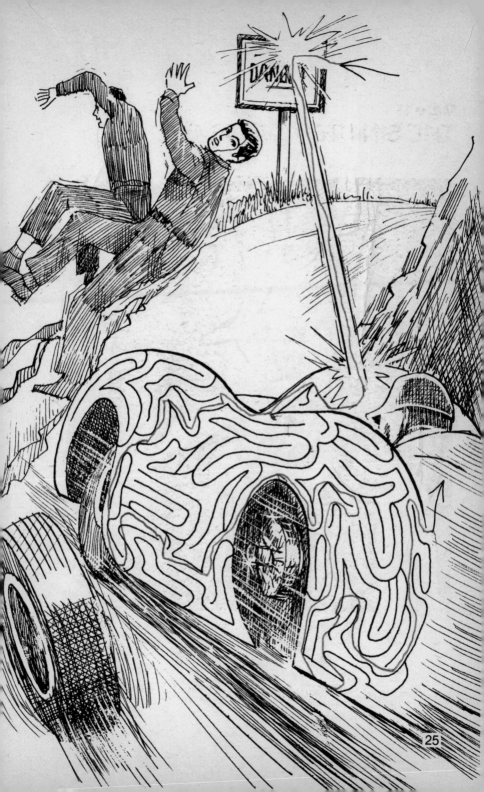

Maze 12
THE MYSTERY OF
CABIN ISLAND

Maze 13

THE CLUE OF
THE BROKEN BLADE

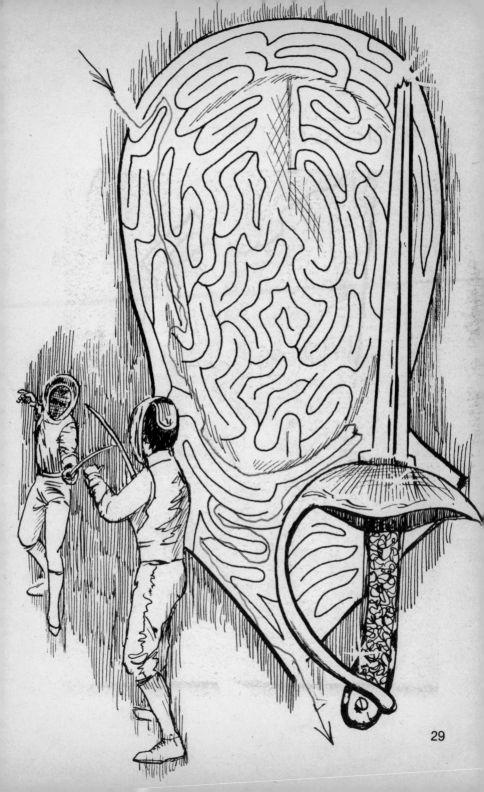

Maze 14
THE WAILING SIREN MYSTERY

Maze 15
THE HOUSE ON THE CLIFF

Maze 16

THE MYSTERY OF
THE FLYING EXPRESS

Maze 17
THE BOMBAY BOOMERANG

Maze 18
THE YELLOW FEATHER MYSTERY

Maze 19
THE SECRET OF
THE LOST TUNNEL

Maze 20
THE ARCTIC PATROL MYSTERY

47

50

8

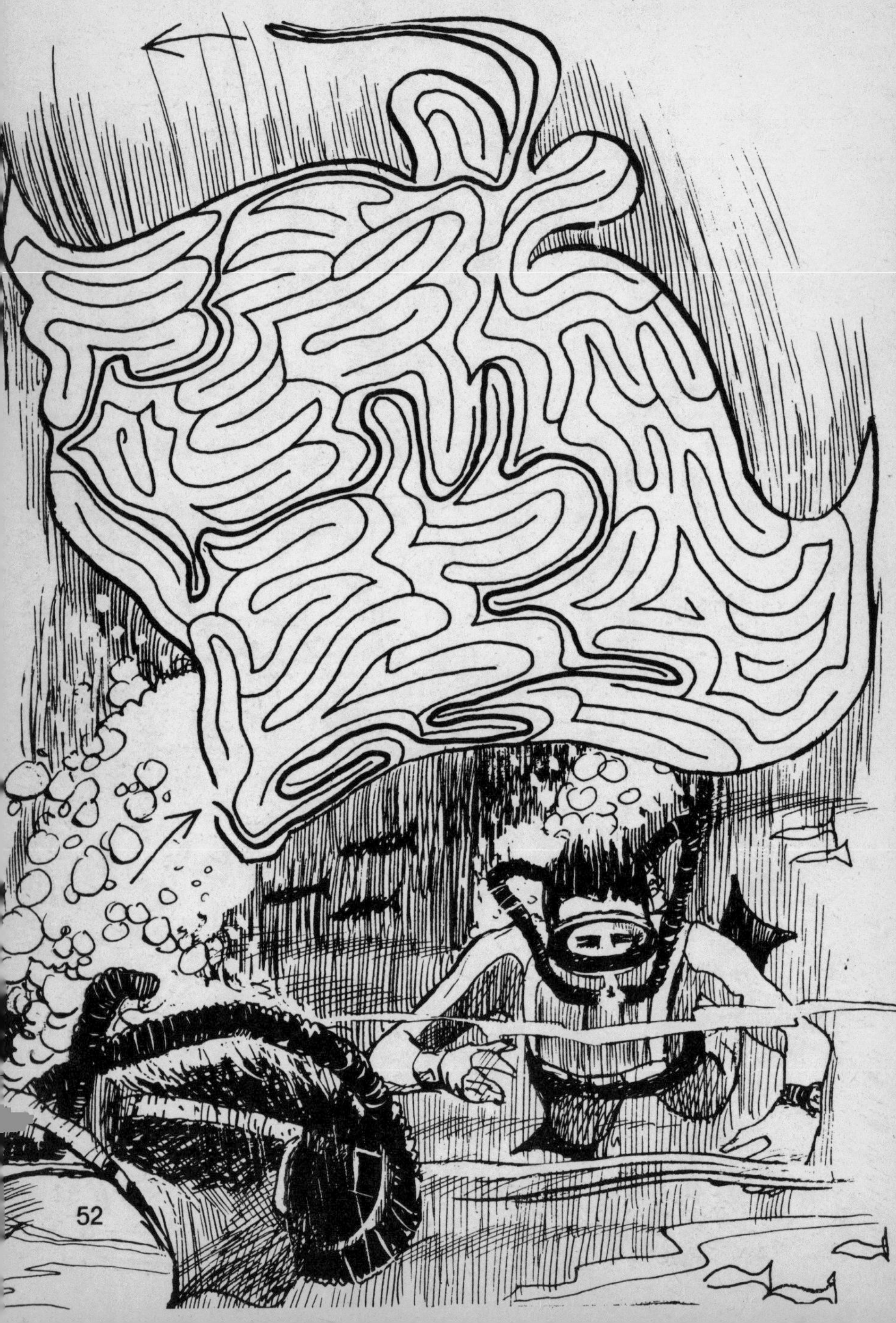

10

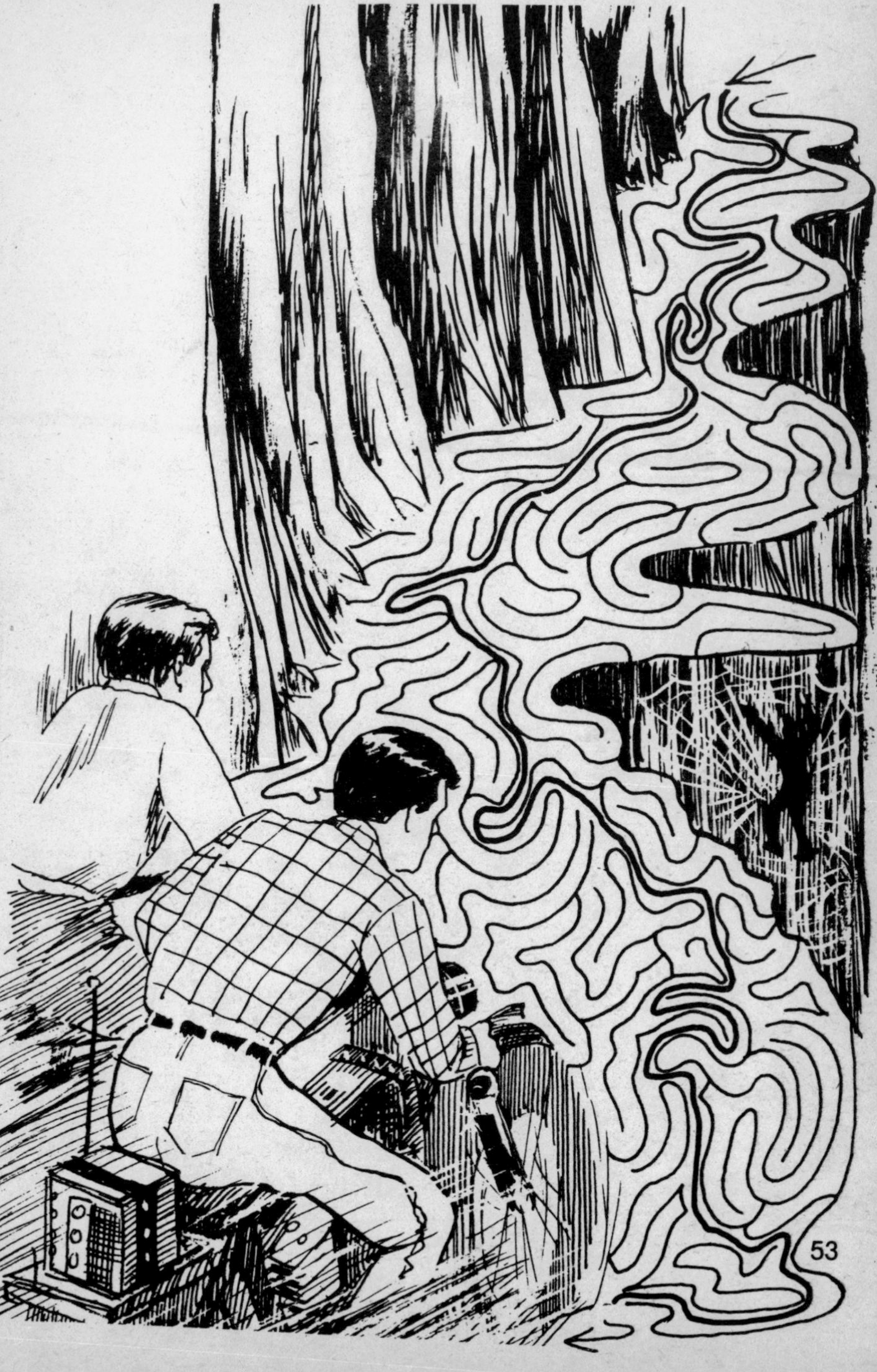

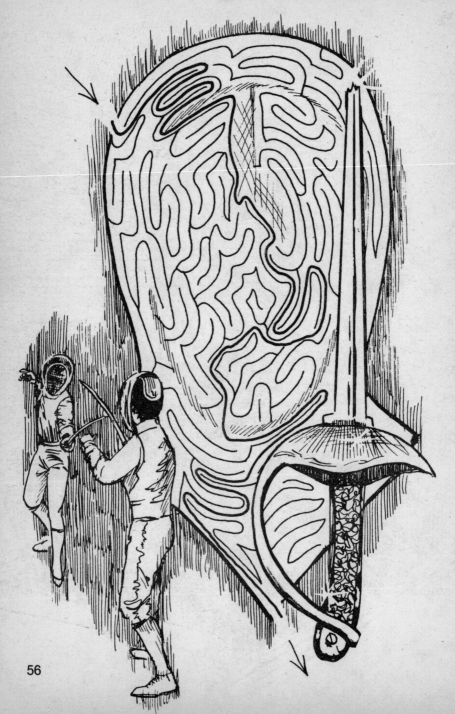

16

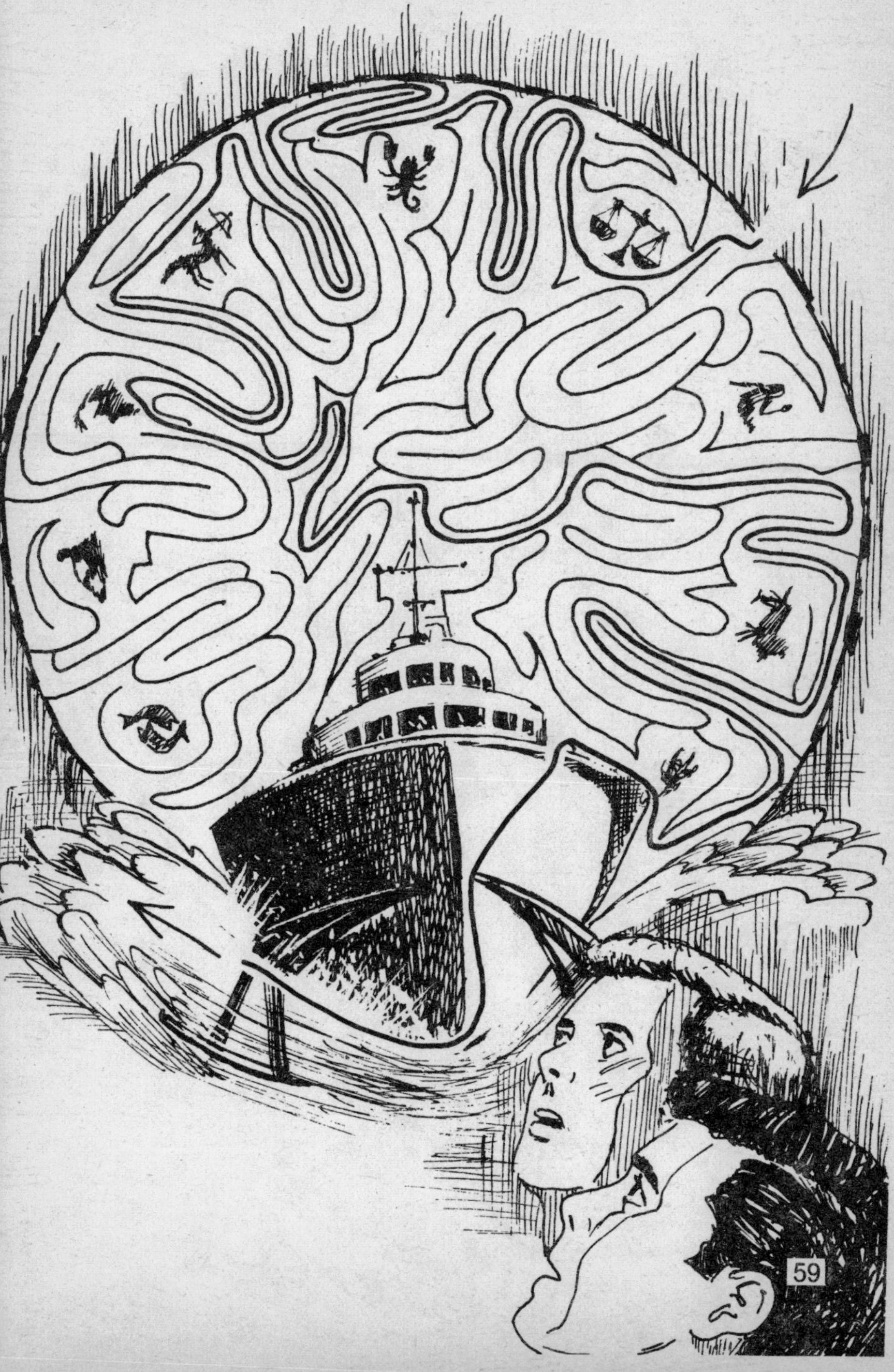

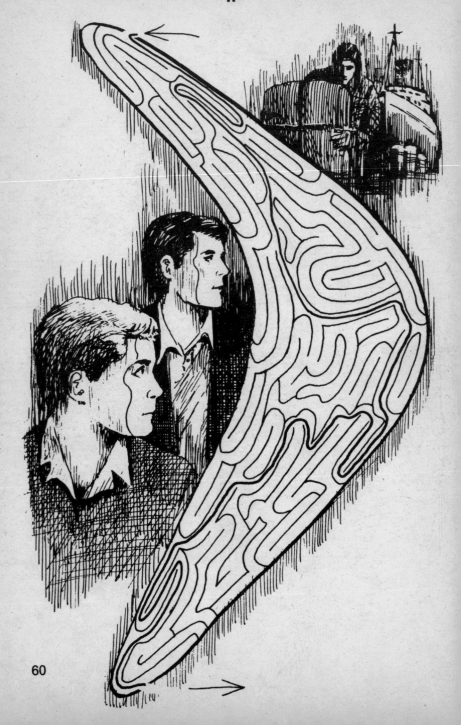

ORDER FORM

HARDY BOYS MYSTERY SERIES

Now that you've had fun with Frank and Joe Hardy, we're sure you'll enjoy reading the famous Hardy Boys mystery and adventure novels.

To make it easy for you to own *all* the books in this exciting series, we've enclosed this handy order form.

56 TITLES AT YOUR BOOKSELLER OR COMPLETE THIS HANDY COUPON AND MAIL TO:

GROSSET & DUNLAP, INC.
P.O. Box 941, Madison Square Post Office, New York, N.Y. 10010

Please send me the Hardy Boys Mystery and Adventure Book(s) checked below @ $2.50 each, plus 25¢ per book postage and handling. My check or money order for $_____ is enclosed. (Please *do not* send cash.)

☐	1.	Tower Treasure	8901-7	☐	29.	The Secret of the Lost Tunnel	8929-7
☐	2.	House on the Cliff	8902-5	☐	30.	Wailing Siren Mystery	8930-0
☐	3.	Secret of the Old Mill	8903-3	☐	31.	Secret of Wildcat Swamp	8931-9
☐	4.	Missing Chums	8904-1	☐	32.	Crisscross Shadow	8932-7
☐	5.	Hunting for Hidden Gold	8905-X	☐	33.	The Yellow Feather Mystery	8933-5
☐	6.	Shore Road Mystery	8906-8	☐	34.	The Hooded Hawk Mystery	8934-3
☐	7.	Secret of the Caves	8907-8	☐	35.	The Clue in the Embers	8935-1
☐	8.	Mystery of Cabin Island	8908-4	☐	36.	The Secrets of Pirates Hill	8936-X
☐	9.	Great Airport Mystery	8909-2	☐	37.	Ghost at Skeleton Rock	8937-8
☐	10.	What Happened At Midnight	8910-6	☐	38.	Mystery at Devil's Paw	8938-6
☐	11.	While the Clock Ticked	8911-4	☐	39.	Mystery of the Chinese Junk	8939-4
☐	12.	Footprints Under the Window	8912-2	☐	40.	Mystery of the Desert Giant	8940-8
☐	13.	Mark on the Door	8913-0	☐	41.	Clue of the Screeching Owl	8941-6
☐	14.	Hidden Harbor Mystery	8914-9	☐	42.	Viking Symbol Mystery	8942-4
☐	15.	Sinister Sign Post	8915-7	☐	43.	Mystery of the Aztec Warrior	8943-2
☐	16.	A Figure in Hiding	8916-5	☐	44.	Haunted Fort	8944-0
☐	17.	Secret Warning	8917-3	☐	45.	Mystery of the Spiral Bridge	8945-9
☐	18.	Twisted Claw	8918-1	☐	46.	Secret Agent on Flight 101	8946-7
☐	19.	Disappearing Floor	8919-X	☐	47.	Mystery of the Whale Tattoo	8947-5
☐	20.	Mystery of the Flying Express	8920-3	☐	48.	The Arctic Patrol Mystery	8948-3
☐	21.	The Clue of the Broken Blade	8921-1	☐	49.	The Bombay Boomerang	8949-1
☐	22.	The Flickering Torch Mystery	8922-X	☐	50.	Danger on Vampire Trail	8950-5
☐	23.	Melted Coins	8923-3	☐	51.	The Masked Monkey	8951-3
☐	24.	Short-Wave Mystery	8924-6	☐	52.	The Shattered Helmet	8952-3
☐	25.	Secret Panel	8925-4	☐	53.	The Clue of the Hissing Serpent	8953-X
☐	26.	The Phantom Freighter	8926-2	☐	54.	The Mysterious Caravan	8954-8
☐	27.	Secret of Skull Mountain	8927-0	☐	55.	The Witchmaster's Key	8955-6
☐	28.	The Sign of the Crooked Arrow	8928-9	☐	56.	The Jungle Pyramid	8956-4

SHIP TO:

NAME _____

(please print)

ADDRESS _____

CITY _____ STATE _____ ZIP _____

T